# A NOTE FROM THE AUTHOR

## WELCOME, MY BEAUTIFUL FRIEND.

Obligation and overcommitment have been the bane of my existence. I was raised to be polite, place others needs before mine, and to not complain about whatever others needs entailed. As a result, I found myself always in what felt like unreciprocating relationships and pouring all of me into other people. It's difficult to admit, but many of the roles I currently play and have played seemed to be fruitless. However, I realized that I could not give all of me, all of the time. I had to humble myself and ask for assistance when needed. But most importantly I had to set boundaries and take care of my physical, emotional, and mental health.

I am a wife, mother, daughter, friend, social worker, and the person people randomly want to share their innermost thoughts with. At times, caring for others has been very overwhelming. My hope is that through this workbook, you are able to love and not loathe the vital role you play as a Caregiver by identifying why you needed to purchase this self-help workbook, expressing your true emotions about the role you have been given, and learning how to provide care for yourself to avoid burnout.

Subscribe to be a member and keep abreast of new courses and books at https://www.thesanctuaryresourcenetwork.net. Let's see where this journey of Care for the Caregiver takes you!

*Jazmin Graham*

Founder of The Sanctuary Resource Network
SPC
Thesanctuaryresourcenetwork.net

# ACKNOWLEDGEMENTS

I dedicate this work to my Caregivers. To my husband: While our roles as Caregivers may vary, you have continuously encouraged me to pursue my dreams. Thank you for your belief in me and my goals. To Sage: You made me a Personal caregiver in 2018. I appreciate you making me step outside of myself and pour all of me into another being. I love you and hope to make you proud.

To my parents, Ronnie and Beverly: I owe you the world. I appreciate your unfailing support. Thank you for standing up for and behind me in every step of my life. To Dexter and Pic: You have adopted me and not treated me as a surrogate child. Thank you for your love and support.
To my extended family: I appreciate your supportive phone calls, text messages and prayers. Your encouragement and unsolicited support is refreshing and unmatched.

To my friends, my tribe, my support system: Thank you for loving and pushing me to be the best version of myself. To my social work colleagues: The world couldn't operate without you. Thank you for standing in the gap for many, working with few resources and conquering the challenges thrown at every turn. My prayer is that through this book, you will all arrive at the mental space you desire.

Thank you to Biz Sister and Gracie Anderson for your assistance with formatting my first work. I couldn't have made this dream reality without you! To Canva and Amazon Kindle Direct Publishing: Thank you for giving me the platform to create my own masterpiece. I owe much gratitude to Ariana Owens, The Innovative Business Coach, Real. Organized. Advocacy, Sherrain Myles Professional Services, and Start Up Greater Good, PBC.

Last but not least, thank you Lord for my talents and gifts. Thank you for allowing me to minister to many through my words.

# TABLE OF CONTENTS

# SECTION ONE
## workbook

# SYSTEMS FAILING

## SECTION INTRODUCTION

*What's Eating Gilbert Grape* is the first movie of my time that pops in my head when I think of the role of Caregivers. Johnny Depp played the role of the oldest son with the weight of his family's needs on his shoulders. His mother was ill and unable to provide the level of care needed to run the household. Therefore, the role of Caregiver was assigned to her oldest son.

Caregiving is a role that does not discriminate. You can be young caring for a parent or grandparent, a professional Caregiver (like myself), or perhaps you're like Johnny Depp and you've been assigned this role. No matter how you became a Caregiver the truth remains that it can be difficult, unrewarding (at times), and emotionally as well as physically taxing.

In the pages ahead, you will describe your personal role as a Caregiver and how you arrived at the emotional space you're in.

# WHY IS MY SYSTEM FAILING?

**QUESTION #1:** What challenges are you struggling with as a Caregiver?

**QUESTION #2:** Where will you be six months from now if you change nothing at all?

# SYSTEMS FAILING

**QUESTION #1:** What do you hope to achieve from working through this book?

**QUESTION #2:** What obstacles do you foresee?

**QUESTION #3:** What efforts could you make to reach your goals and vision?

# SYSTEMS FAILING

It's important to identify the events/circumstances that led to your system failure. Below is a list of triggers that may have contributed to your burnout.

| | | | |
|---|---|---|---|
| Co-dependency | Time Management | Performance Pressure | Boundary Violations |
| Isolation | Criticism | Grief | Overstimulation |
| Health Crises | Financial Burdens | Exhaustion | Lack of Structure/ Routine |
| Insensitivity | Entitlement | Hostility | Invasion of Personal Space |
| Feeling taken for granted | Death | Traumatic Events | Lack of Support |

Albert Ellis' Cognitive Behavioral Therapy (1979), suggests that the events we experience cause us to have certain beliefs, which then yield certain consequences.

**Instructions:** I want you to think about a situation you've encountered and process the activating event which led to certain beliefs and the consequences that followed. On the next page, you will record the situation and map it out.

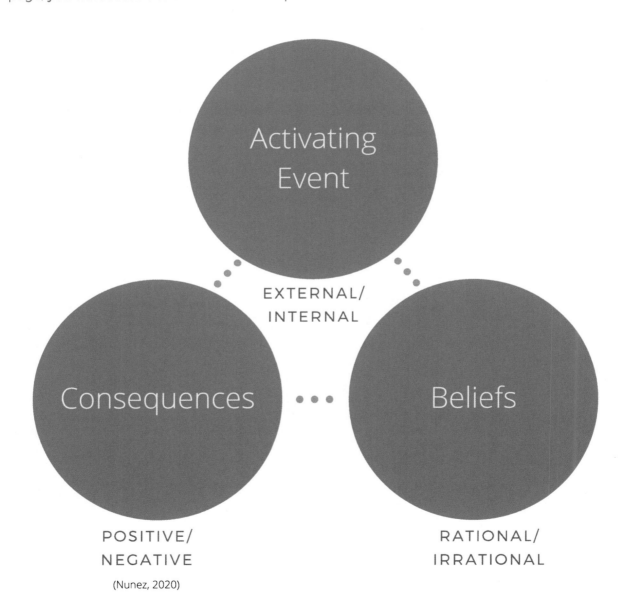

(Nunez, 2020)

# SYSTEMS FAILING

**Instructions**: Record the Activating Event, Beliefs, and Consequences you encountered from the situation noted on the previous page.

Activating Event:

_____

_____

_____

_____

_____

Beliefs:

_____

_____

_____

_____

_____

Consequences:

_____

_____

_____

_____

_____

# COPING SKILLS REVIEW

**Instructions**: Review the list of coping skills below. Check the items that you would consider doing or implementing when you're feeling negatively about your Caregiving role.

Writing

Cooking/baking

Artistic expression

Meditating

Calling a friend

Ripping paper

Aromatherapy

Going for a drive

Yoga

Therapy

Coloring

Photography

Organizing

Finding a hobby

Researching

Watch a comedy

Be in nature

Exercising

Dancing

Doodling

Reading a book

Decorating

Plan an event

Hug someone

Send a letter

Cry

Clean something

Plan a trip

Make a new recipe

Count your blessings

Garden

Donate items

Volunteer

# SYSTEMS FAILING

**QUESTION #1:** What positive coping skills are you currently utilizing?

**QUESTION #2:** What negative coping skills are you currently utilizing?

**QUESTION #3:** What coping skills would you like to gain?

## SELF-REFLECTION

Coping skills are not inherent in humans. Most of us inherit maladaptive behaviors that were demonstrated for us by our families of origin. For instance, I stonewall, shutdown, or pursue arguments as a result of the behaviors demonstrated in my childhood home. As an adult, I've had to learn to identify these behaviors and transform my behavior. How are you coping?

*"The goal isn't to get rid of all your negative thoughts and feelings; that's impossible. The goal is to change your response to them."*
(Chernoff, 2018)

## HAVE QUESTIONS?

Send me a direct message via Instagram or Facebook. You may also send an e-mail via my website. I look forward to hearing from you!

# SECTION TWO
*workbook*

# THIN LINE BETWEEN LOVE &HATE

## SECTION INTRODUCTION

The title of this section rings true to my role as a Caregiver. Let's take my role as a social worker. I have a bleeding heart and passionately desire to help others. However, lately I've been searching for a tourniquet to stop the bleeding. I have days that I see my value and the impact I'm making on my colleagues and clients. Other days, I'm wishing that I could work with robots to preserve my sanity.

Loving and then hating being a Caregiver is not wrong! It's natural and as well as human to feel a spectrum of emotions. I can recall my father providing care to my grandmother who was dying of colon cancer. My Madear was a sassy, dominant, loving and assertive woman. But, her cancer metastasized to her brain and transformed her into a combative woman. My father experienced the brunt of her physical, verbal, and emotional aggression. He watched the endearing mother who raised him become an enraged, helpless, shell of a person. This transformation was heartbreaking and depleted most of his energy. He loved his mother but loathed the woman who was cancer-ridden.

Our experiences mold us into the people we are. Our emotions mold our perceptions and reactions.

# THIN LINE BETWEEN LOVE & HATE

**INSTRUCTIONS:** Sometimes it is difficult to put our emotions into words. Below is a list to assist you with naming your feelings regarding your caregiving role. Check the boxes of the emotions that you identify with.

| | |
|---|---|
| Happy | Weak |
| Peaceful | Rejected |
| Respected | Frustrated |
| Confident | Distant |
| Courageous | Resentful |
| Thankful | Hostile |
| Sensitive | Lonely |
| Optimistic | Vulnerable |
| Inspired | Despair |
| Shocked | Guilty |
| Overwhelmed | Ashamed |
| Pressured | Abandoned |
| Apathetic | Depressed |
| Stressed | Isolated |
| Tired | Victimized |
| Busy | Fearful |
| Helpless | Sad |

# THIN LINE BETWEEN
# LOVE & HATE

**INSTRUCTIONS**: Sometimes we don't know what we are feeling and/or how to express those emotions. Below, are probing questions to aid you in identifying your feelings in regard to being a Caregiver.

**QUESTION #1:**  What emotions can you identify with as a Caregiver?

**QUESTION #2:** Are you accepting or suppressing those emotions?

**QUESTION #3:** Describe the peak of emotion you've felt as a Caregiver.

**QUESTION #4:** Describe the valley of emotion you've felt as a Caregiver.

**QUESTION #5:** What type of Caregiver do you desire to become?

# THIN LINE BETWEEN
# LOVE & HATE

**INSTRUCTIONS:** In the next exercise, you will be asked to list positive affirmations to assist you with getting through the difficult moments of caregiving. Review the list below to give you inspiration.

1. I release my fears and in the process I divulge my stress.
2. I choose to be at peace.
3. I am capable of releasing anger and actively choosing to forgive.
4. I am deserving of all things positive including happiness.
5. I am capable of overcoming the challenges and barriers that I currently face.
6. I choose joy.
7. I release the strongholds that connect me to my negative emotions.
8. I am capable of reframing my negative thoughts and replacing them with positive ones.
9. I am strong, powerful, confident and able to conquer my challenges.
10. I am an overcomer.

# THIN LINE BETWEEN
# LOVE & HATE

**INSTRUCTIONS**: Many of us believe that it's unacceptable to have negative emotions/thoughts regarding our Caregiving roles. Below is your opportunity to counteract those feelings with a positive affirmation.

NEGATIVE THOUGHT:                    POSITIVE AFFIRMATION:

NEGATIVE THOUGHT:                    POSITIVE AFFIRMATION:

NEGATIVE THOUGHT:                    POSITIVE AFFIRMATION:

NEGATIVE THOUGHT:                    POSITIVE AFFIRMATION:

NEGATIVE THOUGHT:                    POSITIVE AFFIRMATION:

# THIN LINE BETWEEN
# LOVE & HATE

**INSTRUCTIONS:** Write a letter to your Caregiver expressing your positive and negative feelings regarding being a Caregiver.

## SELF-REFLECTION

Can I be transparent with you? The road Caregivers travel is difficult at times. There are many variables that contribute to these complexities. You need to know that it's okay if you're not feeling positive about your role every day.

What I have learned is being human means experiencing a gamut of emotions, some times all at once. Extend yourself grace, permit yourself to feel all the feels!

You've got this!

*You're entitled to feel the way you choose to. Let your feelings simmer but not marinate.*

## NEED TO CHAT?

Send me a direct message via Instagram or Facebook. You may also send an e-mail via our website. I look forward to hearing from you!

# SECTION THREE

*workbook*

# IRONIC

## SECTION INTRODUCTION

"I need help," is the hardest phrase to utter when we are Caregivers. We tend to think that asking for assistance makes us inadequate or incompetent. This perspective couldn't be any further from the truth. My mother provided care to my grandmother for approximately 20 years. I remember the day my grandmother moved into the duplex next to my mother like it was yesterday. She was the overseer of all things and provided my mother with emotional support. However, over the years the roles reversed. My mother became responsible for maintaining two households: assisting my grandmother with paying bills, running errands, attending doctor's visits, housekeeping, preparing meals, bathing and grooming her. My mother did everything and anything possible to provide stellar care to her.

But over those twenty years, my mother lost her sense of self and her autonomy. When my grandmother passed in 2019 the most heartbreaking part was that I had to watch my mother grieve the life that she knew and the life that she would never have. You see my mother pressed pause on her life to care for my grandmother. She was heroic in all her efforts but it cost her time that she can never get back. She will admit that she was too proud or ashamed to ask for help and now realizes, Caregivers need care too.

# IRONIC

**INSTRUCTIONS:** Below is a list of what self-care is and isn't. In the space provided below make your own list of what self-care means to you.

### SELF-CARE IS:

- A CHOICE!
- Necessary
- Something you enjoy
- Scheduled/planned
- Something that replenishes your energy
- When your energy causes you to set boundaries

### SELF-CARE IS NOT:

- A one-time, spontaneous event
- A depletion of your energy
- Selfish

# IRONIC

**INSTRUCTIONS**: Write the story you tell yourself and/or others of why you don't need assistance with your caregiving role. Then write the story of how and why you need to ask for assistance with your caregiving role.

OLD STORY

NEW STORY

# I R O N I C

**INSTRUCTIONS**: List the people, agencies, and resources you trust or would like to learn more about that may be able to assist you with your caregiving role.

# IRONIC

**INSTRUCTIONS:** List three activities you can do for self-care as well as the time commitment, the frequency and the emotion the activity will evoke. Remember to only write down activities that you can realistically commit to.

HOW LONG WILL IT TAKE?

5 minutes

15 minutes

30 minutes

45 minutes

ACTIVITY 1:

HOW OFTEN WILL I DO IT?

Daily

Weekly

Monthly

ACTIVITY 2:

HOW DO I WANT TO FEEL?

Joyful

Grateful

Balanced

Relaxed

Loved

ACTIVITY 3:

# IRONIC

**INSTRUCTIONS:** Schedule time to take care of yourself over the next month .

| | WEEK 1 | WEEK 2 | WEEK 3 | WEEK 4 |
|---|---|---|---|---|
| MON | | | | |
| TUES | | | | |
| WED | | | | |
| THURS | | | | |
| FRIDAY | | | | |

## SELF-REFLECTION

I too have allowed shame and pride to keep me from being transparent and asking for assistance, both personally and professionally. Previously, I believed asking for help from friends and family made me vulnerable, and I absolutely hate feeling weak. Professionally, my experience has always been that asking for help is punitive and has caused me to be labeled as incompetent. Therefore, I've have trained myself to struggle instead of stating what I'm experiencing issues with. Today, I challenge you to think of an area in your life where you would benefit from assistance.

Reach out to your support system and ask for what you need!

*"Ask for help. Not because you're weak. But because you want to remain strong.*
*–Les Brown*

### LET ME KNOW WHAT'S ON YOUR MIND!

Send me a direct message via Instagram or Facebook. You may also send an e-mail via our website. I look forward to hearing from you!

# SECTION FOUR

*workbook*

# A CHANGE IS GONNA COME

## SECTION INTRODUCTION

Change is inevitable. Most times we can't anticipate the changes that occur. You have worked diligently to arrive at this point, where you can control the path that caregiving takes you down. This may be your first opportunity to set boundaries and be the Caregiver that you desire to be for yourself and others.

As you continue this caregiving journey, strive for progress, not perfection. Extend yourself grace. On days that you feel overwhelmed lean on your support. When those negative feelings invade your mental space, review the positive affirmations that you wrote.

Caregiving is not a role that expires. Most of us, spend the better part of our lives providing care to someone. In this final chapter, you will catalog what, how, and why you will continue to press forward in your journey toward caring for yourself.

# A CHANGE IS GONNA COME

**INSTRUCTIONS:** Write a letter to yourself affirming the changes you've made to be a better Caregiver to yourself and the plans you have to continue on this journey.

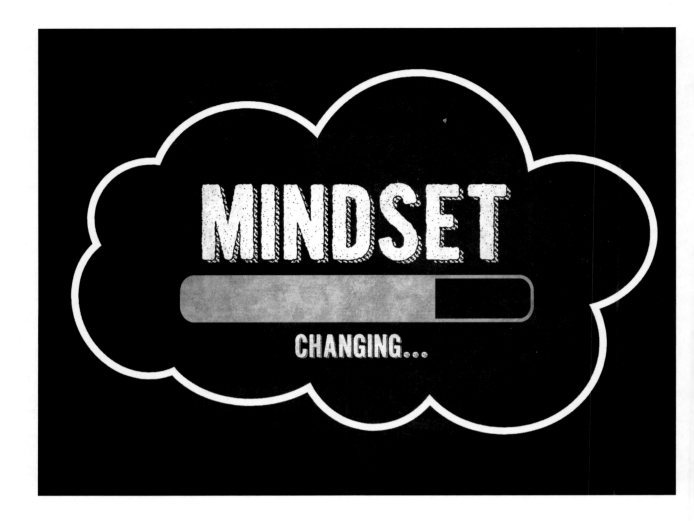

## SELF-REFLECTION

I will be the first to admit change is hard, but it is inevitable. Reframing my thoughts is a practice I implement daily. I literally have to talk to myself out loud some times to process my emotions and filter the negativity out of my mind.

For so long, I allowed negatiivty to take up residence in my heart and mind. I'm a work in progress and want you to know that you can also choose to work on changing your outlook and how you perceive the world around you.

*"Change is the law of life. And those who look only to the past or present are certain to miss the future."*
*(Leipsic, 2016)*

## BE ENCOURAGED!

Send me a direct message via Instagram or Facebook. You may also send an e-mail via our website. I look forward to hearing from you!

# SECTION FIVE
*workbook*

# I'LL BE THERE

I'm proud of you! You've completed this workbook and have hopefully gained some insight regarding your role as a Caregiver. Although you've worked through this book, your journey must continue. Continuing education is of the utmost importance in ensuring that you implement the best practices in self-care. Please, visit: https://thesanctuaryrn.thinkific.com to learn more about our continuing education course offerings.

If you're part of a community agency that is interested in offering continuing education courses to your referral sources, we are able to create courses tailored to your needs to assist with your marketing efforts. Please send your inquiries to: ceu@thesanctuaryresourcenetwork.net.

If you'd like to learn more about The Sanctuary Resource Network SPC's social work consulting packages, you may do so by e-mailing: socialworkconsulting@thesanctuaryresourcenetwork.net or visiting: https://thesanctuaryrn.as.me/schedule.php

We encourage you to provide feedback regarding your reading experience. You may do so by e-mailing: testimonials@thesanctuaryresourcenetwork.net.

You're invited to learn more about the offerings of The Sanctuary Resource Network SPC by becoming a monthly subscriber. Visit thesanctuaryresourcenetwork.net for more information.

# I'LL BE THERE

I am with you in spirit. The resources below are available to you as well:

The Sanctuary Resource Network SPC
https://www.thesanctuaryresourcenetwork.net

National Caregiver Alliance
https://www.caregiving.org

Caregiver Action Network
https://caregiveraction.org

ARCH National Respite Network
https://archrespite.org

## SUPPORT CIRCLE

## SELF-REFLECTION

There have been many times that I've been in a room full of people and still felt alone. I have been home with my daughter and felt alone. I've filled my life with "busy work" to distract myself from my feelings of loneliness. Recently, I've had more than usual downtime and have had to spend a lot of time alone.

This time has been productive and very necessary for my growth. I've learned a lot about myself and my desires. More importantly, I've learned to ask for help and accept it. Today, I charge you with reaching out to your support system and letting them know how you're truly doing.

You don't have to conquer this role alone!

*You're not on this journey alone. There are many who are walking this path with you. Stay the course!*

## KEEP IN TOUCH...

Send me a direct message via Instagram or Facebook. You may also send an e-mail via our website. I look forward to hearing from you!

# REFERENCES

Ballard, G. and Morissette, A. (1996). Ironic. *Jagged Little Pill [CD]*. Hollywood, CA: Maverick and Reprise.

Chernoff, M. & A. (2018). Tweets [Twitter profile]. Retrieved November 25, 2020 from
https://twitter.com/marcandangel/status/962568565231529984?lang=en.

Cooke, S. (1964) . A change Is gonna come. *Ain't that good news [LP]*. Hollywood, CA: RCA.

Jackson 5. (1950). I'll be there. *On Third Album [LP}*. Los Angeles, CA: Motown.

Leipsic, J. (2016). Change is the law of life. And those who look only to the past or present are certain to miss the future. - John F. Kennedy. *Journal of Cardiovascular Computed Tomography. 10.* 10.1016/j.jcct.2016.04.003.

Michael Schenker Group. (1983). Systems failing. *On Built to Destroy [LP}.* London, UK: Chrysalis.

Moon, K. (2012). It's not the load that breaks you down; it's the way you carry it. *The Feminist Wire.* Retrieved November 26, 2020 from https://thefeministwire.com/2012/10/its-not-the-load-that-breaks-you-down-its-the-way-you-carry-it/.

Nunez, K. (2020). What Is the ABC model of Cognitive Behavioral Therapy. *Healthline.* Retrieved November 25, 2020 from https://www.healthline.com/health/abc-model.

The Persuaders. (1971). Thin line between love & hate. *On Thin Line Between Love & Hate [LP]*. New York, NY: Atco/Atlantic Records.

"IT'S NOT THE LOAD THAT BREAKS YOU DOWN. IT'S THE WAY YOU CARRY IT."

LENA HORNE

Made in the USA
Middletown, DE
21 May 2021